We Take a Hike

JENNIFER B. STITH

We can see a lot of things on a hike.

We see bees buzz
and make a hive.

We see five mice sit
in a line.

We see a vine go
up a rock.

9

We see a pine on
the side of a lake.

We see kids ride on
a bike path.

That was a nice hike!

bike	line	ride
five	mice	side
hike	nice	vine
hive	pine	

Decodable Words

bee(s)	lake	see
buzz	lot	sit
can	make	take
go	on	up
in	rock	we
kid(s)		

High-Frequency Words

a	path	thing(s)
and	that	was
of	the	